IGOR STRAVINSKY
1882-

MAURICE RAVEL
1875-1937

BRUNO HUHN
1871-

VERNON DUKE
1903-

SERGE PROKOFIEFF
1891-1953

VICTOR HERBERT
1859-1924

ALEC TEMPLETON
1910-

ALEXANDER SCRIABIN
1872-1915

The SCRIBNER MUSIC LIBRARY

EDITED BY

JOHN TASKER HOWARD

Volume IX: Supplementary Compositions

PIANO & VOCAL

CHARLES SCRIBNER'S SONS, NEW YORK

THE SCRIBNER MUSIC LIBRARY

VOLUME IX — SUPPLEMENTARY COMPOSITIONS

TABLE OF CONTENTS — TITLES

TABLE OF CONTENTS — COMPOSERS

The titles of piano compositions are printed in roman type and the titles of vocal numbers in italics.

A Guide Through Volume IX

THE volumes of The SCRIBNER MUSIC LIBRARY are devoted entirely to compositions which are heard constantly over the great broadcasting chains—played by orchestras, chamber music organizations, or instrumental soloists; sung by choral organizations or by vocal soloists. Each of the volumes contains only the choicest and most popular of its particular type of music.

This volume supplements the first eight volumes of the series first by supplying a number of older representative compositions which were not included in the earlier volumes, and secondly, by adding a large number of contemporary and recent pieces which have become widely used by broadcasting stations. Among the latter are a number of copyright works by American composers which are presented with the permission of the copyright owners.

STANDARD PIANO COMPOSITIONS
Volume I already contains a charming piece by Domenico Scarlatti, and to this is added, in Volume IX, his lovely **Pastorale** in the famous arrangement by Carl Taussig. To the Mozart list has been added the dramatic **Fantasie No. 3 in D Minor,** long a favorite with pianists, while Beethoven's representation in the series has been increased by the melodious **Rondo in C Major.** Volume I has also a generous collection of Chopin works, but no **Polonaise,** so Volume IX offers the stirring **Military Polonaise in A Major,** which is heard frequently on the air, not only as a piano piece but also in orchestral form. This is followed by one of the most beautiful pieces Schumann ever composed, his **Romance in F Sharp,** Op. 28, No. 2. The 19th-Century American romanticist, Louis Moreau Gottschalk, is represented by his restful **Berceuse,** which is based on an old French folk-song. Two of Tschaikowsky's most popular works are the first **Piano Concerto in B Flat Minor, Op. 23,** and the **Fantasy Overture, Romeo and Juliet.** These works are familiar not only in their original form, but also through the numerous popular songs that have been adapted from their principal themes. They are presented here in solo piano arrangements. Next come four piano pieces by Russian composers: a quiet, restful **Nocturne** by Alexander Borodin; then two pieces by Alexander Scriabin—the **Prelude** and **Nocturne** from Op. 9, originally composed for the left-hand alone (those who find it too difficult to play the pieces in this manner may play them with both hands); and after these the famous **Orientale by** César Cui. The American Edward MacDowell is represented by two of his best-known works—— **A.D.MDCXX,** from his **Sea Pieces,** Op. 55, a tone-picture of the Pilgrims' voyage in the Mayflower; and an effective number from **Woodland Sketches,** Op. 51——**From an Indian Lodge.** These are followed by the stately and beautiful **Pavane** by the French modernist, Maurice Ravel. This piece is often heard also as an orchestral composition, and it formed the basis of a recent popular song—"The Lamp is Low." Turning again to the Russians, the modern group ends with a simplified arrangement of themes from Serge Prokofieff's Musical Fairy Tale for Children, **Peter and the Wolf,** and an altogether modernistic **Prelude in E Flat, Op. 34, No. 19,** by the widely-discussed Soviet composer, Dmitri Shostakovitch.

EXCERPTS FROM BALLETS
The older ballets are already well represented in Volume V. This Volume, therefore, presents excerpts from two modern ballets: Claude Debussy's impressionistic **Prelude to the Afternoon of a Faun;** and **Dance of the Princesses** and **Berceuse** from **The Firebird,** by the famous Russian composer, Igor Stravinsky.

EXCERPTS FROM GRAND OPERA
The comprehensive list in Volume IV of excerpts from Grand Operas, arranged for piano, is supplemented in this Volume by the Overture from Michail Glinka's **Russlan and Ludmilla,** in itself a most popular concert piece; and by selections from two additional Wagner operas — **The Prelude** and **Love Death** from **Tristan and Isolda;** and **Ride of the Valkyries** and **Magic Fire Music** from **The Valkyries.**

EXCERPTS FROM LIGHT OPERA
In this Volume a famous American operetta is added to the Light Operas of Volume V — **The Belle of New York,** by Gustave Kerker, which enjoyed popularity at the Casino Theatre, New York, in 1908, and then ran for more than two years in London. A motion picture based on this operetta has been made.

LIGHT PIANO COMPOSITIONS
All but one of the Light Compositions in Volume IX are composed by foreign-born composers who made their homes in America. Luigi Arditi, composer of the famous **Il Bacio (The Kiss),** lived for a number of years in New York. **Il Bacio** is followed by **La Serenata, Op. 3,** by the beloved Victor Herbert. Next comes a **Brooklyn Barcarolle** by Vernon Duke, a composer of popular music who also writes serious works under his real name, Vladimir Dukelsky. The famous blind composer-pianist, Alec

Templeton, contributes his famous satire, **Mozart Matriculates** (you'll recognize its melody as that of **The Marine's Hymn**), and a charming **Lullaby** which he composed as a child. In contrast, **Handful of Keys,** by the late Thomas (Fats) Waller, famous Negro composer-pianist, is a characteristically modern piece in popular style.

MODERN DANCE MUSIC

The waltzes, polkas, and two-steps of Volume VI are supplemented by four modern Latin-American dance pieces: **La Cumparsita**, a Tango by Matos Rodriguez; **Adios**, a Rhumba by Enric Madriguera; **Amor**, a Bolero by Gabriel Ruiz; and **Tico-Tico**, a Samba by Zequinha Abreu.

SACRED MUSIC FOR THE PIANO

The instrumental contents of the book close with three sacred compositions for piano: first, a solo piano arrangement of **Cujus Animam** from Rossini's **Stabat Mater**; secondly, **Still Waters** by John Tasker Howard, a Reverie on a 17th-Century tune which the Puritans sang to the 23rd Psalm; and, lastly, **At the Convent** by Alexander Borodin.

SACRED SONGS

The vocal section opens with a solo arrangement of a Choral from J. S. Bach's Cantata No. 147, the lovely and justly famous **Jesu, Joy of Man's Desiring**. Next comes Schubert's **Ave Maria**. This piece is already included in Volume VII as a piano solo, but in this Volume it appears in its original form as a song, followed by the **Panis Angelicus** from César Franck's **Messe Solennelle**, and the **Agnus Dei** of Georges Bizet.

HYMNS

Three widely-used Catholic hymns open this section: **O Sacred Head; Jesus, My Lord, My God, My All;** and **Holy God, We Praise Thy Name.** Then comes the stirring **Rejoice, Ye Pure in Heart** and **Stand Up For Jesus**, the lovely **Saviour Again to Thy Dear Name**, and the hymn which was universally adopted by the WAVES during World War No. II, **Eternal Father Strong to Save.** The hymn section closes with the popular gospel hymn — **The Old Rugged Cross.**

CONCERT SONGS

Two famous songs which were not included in Volume VIII head the list of Concert Songs: Schumann's dramatic **The Two Grenadiers**, and **Allerseelen (All Soul's Day)** by Richard Strauss. Both songs are printed with English texts. Then comes a group of songs by contemporary American composers, starting with a whimsical dialect song by Tom Waring — **Ol' Darkie, Ol' Mule.** Waring is a brother of Fred Waring, whose orchestra and glee club are popular on the air and on phonograph records. Two more dialect songs come next: **Abraham** by Robert MacGimsey, and **Mistah Shakespeah** by Charles Wakefield Cadman. The distinguished American composer, Henry K. Hadley, is represented by **Forever and a Day**; Bruno Huhn by one of America's most popular concert songs, the dramatic **Invictus**; Ethelbert Nevin by his **Serenade (Good Night! Good Night, Beloved!)**; and Mana-Zucca by her setting of a Browning poem, **Grow Old Along with Me.** The section closes with two lighter concert songs, standard favorites — **Marcheta** by Victor Schertzinger and **A Little Bit of Heaven** by Ernest R. Ball.

BALLADS AND FOLK-SONGS

At this point Volume IX turns to popular selections which are universally featured not only on the air but wherever there is any kind of music. First comes a song which helped to create the vogue for sentimental story-ballads — Charles K. Harris's **After the Ball**, which has become a classic. This is followed by two traditional Cowboy songs — **Home on the Range** and the Dogie song, **Whoopee Ti Yi Yo. Take Me Back to My Boots and Saddle** is a popular song in the Cowboy idiom; **Deep in the Heart of Texas** was heard on the radio dozens of times each day in the early 1940's; and **You Are My Sunshine,** which completes this classification, is a popular song in group-singing.

PLANTATION AND MINSTREL SONGS

The first three songs in this category are old-timers. **Buffalo Gals** is an adaptation of **Lubly Fan,** a minstrel song which was first published more than a hundred years ago. Its refrain "Won't you come out tonight," was adapted to a popular song. James A. Bland's **Carry Me Back to Old Virginny** was originally written for the minstrel shows in the late 1870's, and is now the official state song of Virginia. **Waiting for the Robert E. Lee** was first published in 1912. It was the hit-song of that year and has retained its popularity. The modern song in this group is Hoagy Carmichael's and Johnny Mercer's **Lazybones,** an outstanding favorite.

PATRIOTIC SONGS

Volume IX concludes with four Patriotic Songs which were not included in the patriotic material of Volume VIII: **America the Beautiful,** with words by Katharine Lee Bates; Mathias Keller's **The American Hymn**; and two famous service songs — **The Caissons Go Rolling Along** (Artillery), and **The Marine's Hymn.**

COMPLETE INDEX

This volume also contains a Complete Index to all of the volumes, cross-referenced so that all important compositions can be found under either their titles or composers; there are also a biographical, pronouncing dictionary, and a glossary of musical terms.

Pastorale

Arranged by Carl **Tausig**.

DOMENICO SCARLATTI

ral - lentan-do (una corda)   a tempo

Fantasie No. 3

W. A. MOZART

Rondo

L. VAN BEETHOVEN, Op. 51, N° 1

Polonaise
(Military)

FRÉDÉRIC CHOPIN, Op. 40, No 1.

Romance

ROBERT SCHUMANN Op. 28, № 2

Berceuse
(Cradle Song)

L. M. GOTTSCHALK

Romeo and Juliet

Fantasy Overture

Selected Themes

PETER I. TSCHAIKOWSKY

Concerto No. I, in B Flat Minor
Selected Themes

P. I. TSCHAIKOWSKY, OP. 23

Andante non troppo

Andantino semplice

Allegro con fuoco

Nocturne
From "Petite Suite"

ALEXANDER BORODIN

*Prélude

ALEXANDER SCRIABIN Op. 9 Nº 1

* This Prélude, and the Nocturne which follows, were composed for the left hand alone. They may however, be played by both hands.

*Nocturne

ALEXANDER SCRIABIN, Op.9 No.2

★This Nocturne, and the preceding Prélude, were composed for the left hand alone. They may however, be played by both hands.

Orientale

From "Kaleidoscope"

CÉSAR CUI, Op. 50, No. 9

A. D. MDCXX

From "Sea Pieces"

The yellow setting sun
Melts the lazy sea to gold
And gilds the swaying galleon
That towards a land of promise
Lunges hugely on.

EDWARD MAC DOWELL
Op. 55, No 3.

In unbroken rolling rhythm. ($\sqrt{ } = 58$)

Softly with ponderous swing.

From an Indian Lodge

From "Woodland Sketches"

EDWARD MAC DOWELL, Op. 51, No. 5

*) The low notes of the octaves carry the melody

*) The upper notes of the octaves carry the melody $\qquad$ etc.

Pavane

MAURICE RAVEL

Editor's note: If stretches are too wide for small hands, notes in parentheses ( ) may be omitted.

Tempo primo

melodia marcata

Peter and the Wolf
(A Musical Tale for Children)
Selected Melodies

SERGE PROKOFIEFF

70

(The Cat)

(The Procession)

L'istesso Tempo (The Duck)

(The Procession)

Prelude

DMITRI SHOSTAKOVITCH
Op. 34, No. 19

Prelude to the Afternoon of a Faun

Selected Themes

CLAUDE DEBUSSY

The Firebird
Selected Themes

IGOR STRAVINSKY

Russlan and Ludmilla

Selections from the Overture

MICHAIL GLINKA

Presto M.M. ♩ = 140.

Tristan and Isolda

Selected Themes

RICHARD WAGNER

Lento e languido (Prelude)

Molto moderato (Isolda's Love-Death)

The Valkyries
Selected Themes

RICHARD WAGNER

(Magic Fire Scene)

The Belle of New York

Selected Melodies

GUSTAVE KERKER

Moderato (*La Belle Parisienne.*)

Moderato *(When we are married)*

Amoroso

Andante (*My Little Baby*)

Largamente (*Dance*)

Very slow Waltz tempo (*They call me the Belle of New York.*)

Il Bacio

(The Kiss)

Waltz

LUIGI ARDITI

La Serenata

VICTOR HERBERT, OPUS 3

Brooklyn Barcarolle

VERNON DUKE

Mozart Matriculates

ALEC TEMPLETON

A Lullaby

ALEC TEMPLETON

Change Pedal after each change of Harmony.

Handful of Keys

Arranged by
FRANK WELDON

THOMAS (FATS) WALLER

"Play Harlem"

La Cumparsita

Tango

MATOS RODRIGUEZ

Adios

Rhumba

ENRIC MADRIGUERA

Moderato assai

Amor

Bolero

GABRIEL RUIZ

Tempo di Beguine

Tico - Tico
Samba

ZEQUINHA ABREU

Cujus Animam
(Stabat Mater)

GIOACCHINO ROSSINI

Still Waters
(Reverie on a Psalm Tune)

JOHN TASKER HOWARD

✱ > Marks indicate melody.

At the Convent

From "Petite Suite"

ALEXANDER BORODIN

Andante religioso

Jesu, Joy of Man's Desiring

Chorale from Cantata No. 147, Arranged for
Solo Voice and Piano

J. S. BACH

soar - ing, dy - ing round __ Thy
in the love of joys __ un -

throne.
known.

Ave Maria

FRANZ SCHUBERT

m:d _____ des-pair. Safe may we sleep un-til the

mor - row, Though ban - ish'd, out-cast and re-vil'd. Oh

Maid - en, see a maid-en's sor - row; Oh Moth - er, hear a suppliant

child! A - ve Ma - ri - -

a!

Panis Angelicus
(Messe Solennelle)

English Version by
Sigmund Spaeth

CÉSAR FRANCK

pau - per Ser - vus et hu - mi - lis.
hum - bly, Low - ly tho' he may be.

Pa - nis an -
O sa - cred

ge - li - cus Fit pa - nis ho - mi - num Dat pa - nis
bread of life, Made mor - tal from a - bove, Bread with sal -

coe - li - cus fi - gu - ris ter - mi - num. O res mi -
va - tion rife, The pledge of heav'n - ly love. O won - drous

Agnus Dei
(Lamb of God)

GEORGES BIZET

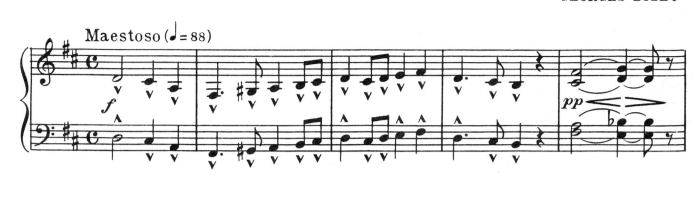

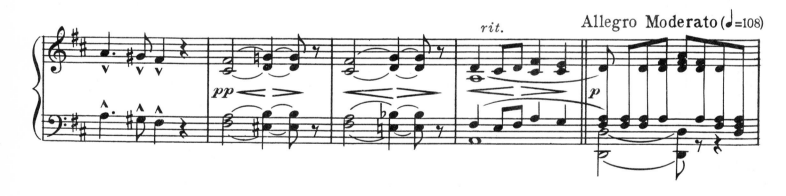

A - gnus De - i! qui tol - lis pecca - ta mun - di,
Lamb____ of God, thou that tak-est a-way the world's guilt,

O Sacred Head

(Salve Caput Cruentatum)

1. O Sacred Head surrounded By crown of piercing thorn!
2. I see Thy strength and vigor All fading in the strife,
3. In this Thy bitter passion Good Shepherd think of me,

O bleeding Head, so wounded, Reviled and put to scorn!
And death with cruel rigor Bereaving Thee of life;
With Thy most sweet compassion, Unworthy though I be;

Death's pallid hue comes o'er Thee, The glow of life decays,
O agony and dying! O love to sinners free!
Beneath Thy Cross abiding, Forever would I rest,

Yet angel hosts adore Thee, And tremble as they gaze.
Jesu, all grace supplying, O turn Thy face on me.
In Thy dear love confiding, And with Thy presence blest.

Jesus, My Lord, My God, My All

1. Je - sus, my Lord _ my God _ my All! _ How can I
2. Had I but Ma - ry's sin - less heart, To love Thee
3. Oh! see up - on _ the al - tar placed The Vic - tim
4. Je - sus, dear Pas - tor of _ the flock, We crowd in

love Thee as I ought? And how re - vere _ this
with, my dear - est King; Oh! with what bursts _ of
of di - vin - est love! Let all the earth _ be to
love a - bout Thy feet; Our voic - es yearn _ to

won - drous gift, _ So far sur - pass - ing hope or thought?
fer - vent praise, Thy good-ness, Je - sus, would I sing.
low _ a - dore, And join the choirs of heav'n a - bove.
praise Thee, Lord, And joy - ful - ly Thy pres - ence greet.

Sweet Sac - ra - ment, We Thee _ a - dore; _ Oh! make us love Thee

more _ and more; Oh! make us love Thee more _ and more.

Holy God, We Praise Thy Name

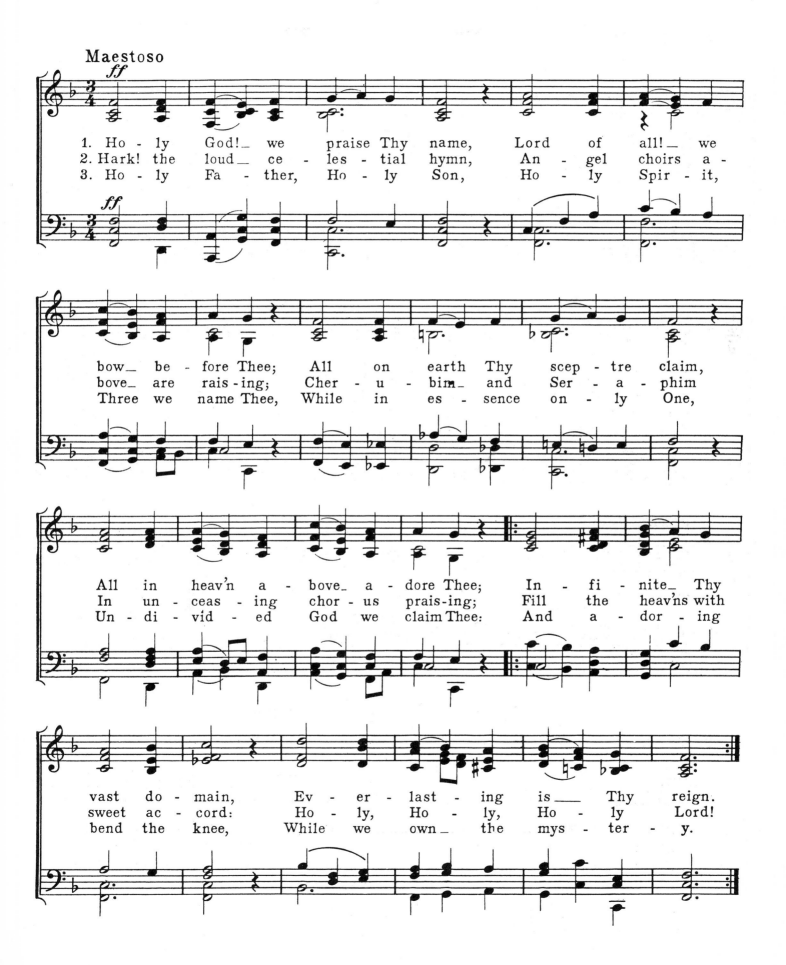

1. Ho - ly God!_ we praise Thy name, Lord of all!_ we
2. Hark! the loud_ ce - les - tial hymn, An - gel choirs a -
3. Ho - ly Fa - ther, Ho - ly Son, Ho - ly Spir - it,

bow_ be - fore Thee; All on earth Thy scep - tre claim,
bove_ are rais - ing; Cher - u - bim_ and Ser - a - phim
Three we name Thee, While in es - sence on - ly One,

All in heav'n a - bove_ a - dore Thee; In - fi - nite_ Thy
In un - ceas - ing chor - us prais - ing; Fill the heav'ns with
Un - di - vid - ed God we claim Thee: And a - dor - ing

vast do - main, Ev - er - last - ing is___ Thy reign.
sweet ac - cord: Ho - ly, Ho - ly, Ho - ly Lord!
bend the knee, While we own_ the mys - ter - y.

Rejoice, Ye Pure in Heart

EDWARD H. PLUMPTRE

ARTHUR M. MESSITER

1. Re - joice, ye__ pure in heart, Re - joice, give thanks and sing:
2. With all the__ an - gel choirs, With all the saints on earth,
3. Still lift your__ stand - ard high, Still march in firm ar - ray;
4. Yes, on through life's long path, Still chant - ing as ye go;
5. Then on, ye__ pure in heart, Re - joice, give thanks, and sing;

Your fes - tal ban - ner wave on high, The cross of Christ your King.
Pour out the strains of joy and bliss, True rap - ture, no - blest mirth!
As war - riors through the dark - ness toil Till dawns the gold - en day.
From youth to age, by night and day, In glad-ness and in woe.
Your fes - tal ban - ner wave on high, The cross of Christ your King.

REFRAIN

Re - joice, re - joice, Re - joice, give thanks, and sing! A - men.

Re - joice, re - joice,

Stand Up for Jesus

GEORGE DUFFIELD

GEORGE J. WEBB

1. Stand up, stand up for Je - sus, Ye sol - diers of the cross, Lift high His roy - al
2. Stand up, stand up for Je - sus, The trump - et call o - bey; Forth to the might - y
3. Stand up, stand up for Je - sus, Stand in His strength a - lone; The arm of flesh will
4. Stand up, stand up for Je - sus, The strife will not be long; This day the noise of

ban - ner, It must not suf - fer loss; From vic - tory un - to vic - tory, His
con - flict, In this His glor - ious day. "Ye, that are men, now serve Him", A -
fail you__Ye dare not trust your own; Put on the gos - pel ar - mor, Each
bat - tle, The next, the vic - tor's song; To him that o - ver - com - eth, A

ar - my shall He lead, Till ev - ery foe is van-quished And Christ is Lord in-deed.
gainst un-num-bered foes; Let cour-age rise with dan - ger, And strength to strength op-pose.
piece put on with prayer; Where du - ty calls, or dan - ger, Be nev - er want-ing there.
crown of life shall be; He with the King of glo - ry Shall reign e - ter - nal-ly. A-men.

Saviour Again to Thy Dear Name

JOHN ELLERTON   EDWARD J. HOPKINS

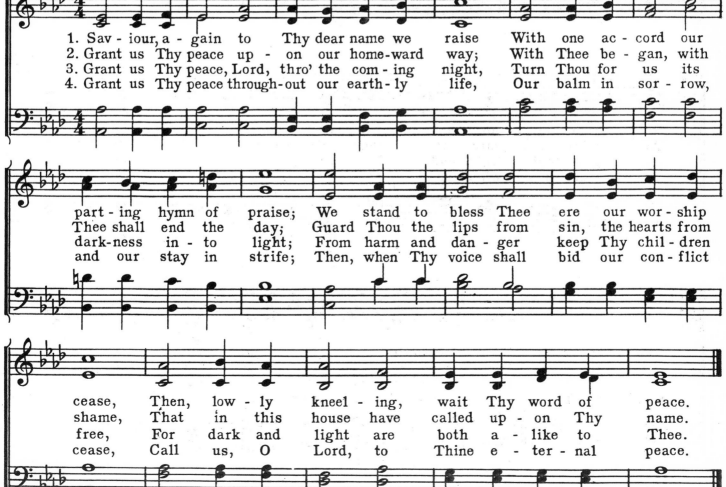

1. Sav - iour, a - gain to Thy dear name we raise With one ac - cord our
2. Grant us Thy peace up - on our home-ward way; With Thee be - gan, with
3. Grant us Thy peace, Lord, thro' the com - ing night, Turn Thou for us its
4. Grant us Thy peace through-out our earth - ly life, Our balm in sor - row,

part - ing hymn of praise; We stand to bless Thee ere our wor - ship
Thee shall end the day; Guard Thou the lips from sin, the hearts from
dark - ness in - to light; From harm and dan - ger keep Thy chil - dren
and our stay in strife; Then, when Thy voice shall bid our con - flict

cease, Then, low - ly kneel - ing, wait Thy word of peace.
shame, That in this house have called up - on Thy name.
free, For dark and light are both a - like to Thee.
cease, Call us, O Lord, to Thine e - ter - nal peace.

Eternal Father, Strong to Save

WILLIAM WHITING

JOHN B. DYKES

With dignity

1. E - ter - nal Fa - ther, strong to save, Whose arm doth bind the
2. O Sav - iour, whose al - might - y word The winds and waves sub -
3. O sa - cred Spir - it, who didst brood Up - on the cha - os
4. O Trin - i - ty of love and power, Our breth - ren shield in

rest - less wave, Who bidd'st the might - y o - cean deep
mis - sive heard, Who walk - edst on the foam - ing deep
dark and rude, Who bad'st its an - gry tu - mult cease,
dan - ger's hour; From rock and tem - pest, fire and foe,

Its own ap - point - ed lim - its keep: O hear us when we
And calm a - mid its rage didst sleep: O hear us when we
And gav - est light and life and peace: O hear us when we
Pro - tect them wher - so - e'er they go; And ev - er let there

cry to Thee For those in per - il on the sea.
cry to Thee For those in per - il on the sea.
cry to Thee For those in per - il on the sea.
rise to Thee Glad hymns of praise from land and sea. A - men.

The Old Rugged Cross

Rev. GEO. BENNARD

The Two Grenadiers

HEINRICH HEINE

ROBERT SCHUMANN

To France were re-turn-ing two gren-a-diers, In Rus - sia they both had been tak - en, And when they came to the Ger-man fron-tier Their cour - age was sad - ly shak - en, 'Twas there that they both heard the sor - row-ful tale, That

France's proud realm had been shak--en, De - feat - ed and scat - ter'd the val - i - ant'host, And the emp-'ror, the emp-'ror'd been tak-en.

How bit - ter-ly wept then the gren-a - diers, At hear-ing the ter - ri-ble sto - ry; And one then said: "A-las! once more My wounds are bleed-ing and

Em - per-or sighs in a pris - on! O grant me, broth-er, but one

prayer, If my hours I now must num - ber, Take

with thee my bod-y to my na - tive land, In France let me peace - ful-ly

Più mosso

slum - ber. My cross of hon-or with rib-bon red,

tramp-ing of neigh-ing hors-es. Then o - ver my grave will my Em-per-or ride, While

swords gleam bright-ly and rat - tle, While swords gleam bright-ly and

rat - tle; Then arm'd to the teeth will I rise from the grave, For my

Emp'ror, my Emp'ror to bat-tle.

Allerseelen
(All Soul's Day)

HERMANN VON GILM
English version by
Sigmund Spaeth

RICHARD STRAUSS
Op. 10, No. 8

Bring back to life   a fra-grant mem-'ry's

tok - en, The last red flow'rs of grief be-side me lay,   And let our words of love a - gain   be

Ol' Darkie, Ol' Mule

JACK DOLPH   TOM WARING

Ol' grey dark-ie, ol' _____ grey mule, __

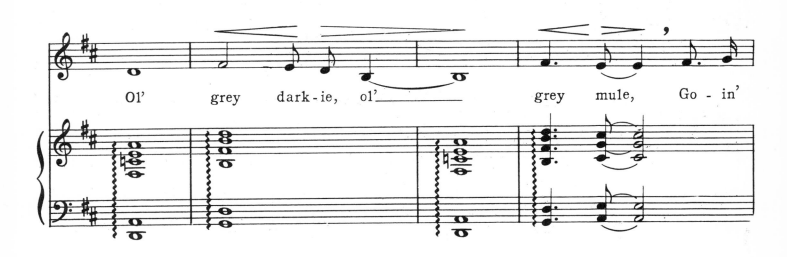

Ol' grey dark-ie, ol' _____ grey mule, Go-in'

192

Abraham

ROBERT MAC GIMSEY

I'm goin' to rest on the bo-som of Ab-ra-ham, Ab-ra-ham, Ab - ra-ham, I'm goin' to
I'm goin' to eat at the ta-ble with Ab-ra-ham, Ab-ra-ham, Ab - ra-ham, And I'll have
I'm goin' to walk a-round hea-ven with Ab-ra-ham, Ab-ra-ham, Ab - ra-ham, Walk down the

rest on the bo-som of Ab - ra-ham, When the an-gels car-ry me home, I'm goin' to
chick - en, am-bro-si - a and ho-ney lamb, When the an-gels car-ry me home, I'm goin' to
streets that are paved — with gold, ——— When the an-gels car-ry me home, I'm goin' to

Mistah Shakespeah

HAZEL DELL CRANDALL

CHARLES WAKEFIELD CADMAN

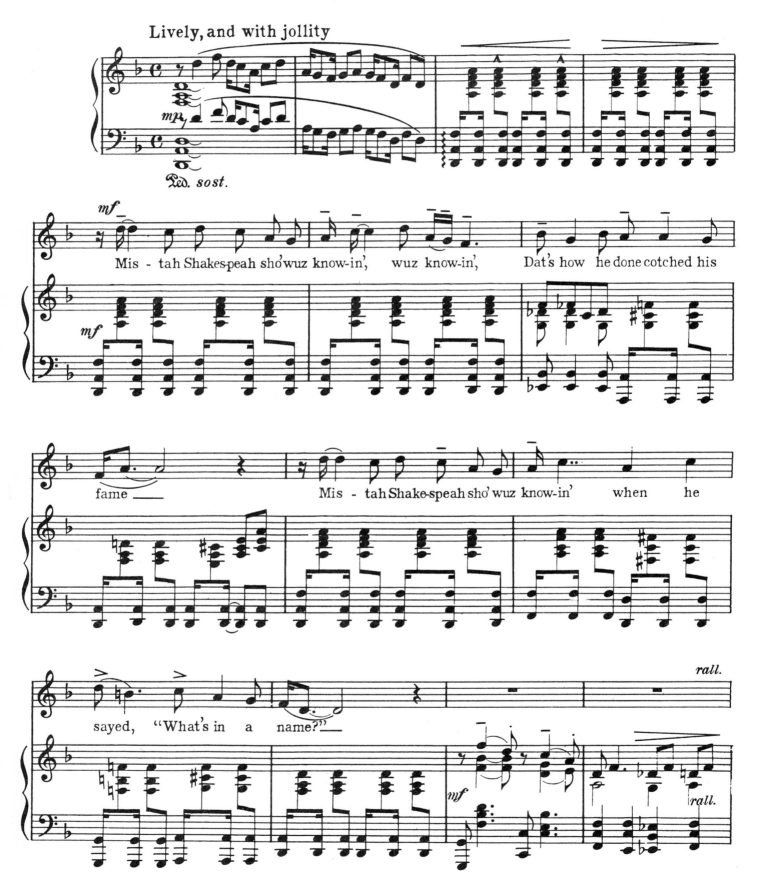

She done weigh mos' nigh th'ee hun - dered: Be - fo' huh feet's growed to de

groun'._____ Dah's mah Mis-sus,

Huh name's An-gel. Laws, ef up_ dah in_ de_ skies Dem dah an-gels is

all lak huh, Laws Ah prays Ah nev-ah dies, Ah prays Ah nev-ah

Forever and a Day

THOMAS BAILEY ALDRICH

HENRY K. HADLEY, Op. 12, No. 1

I lit-tle know or care If the black-bird on the bough Is fill-ing all the air With his soft cre-scen-dos

Words used by permission of the Author.

now; For she is gone a - way, And when she went she took The spring-time in her look, The peach - blow on her cheek, The laugh - ter from the brook, The blue from out the May And what she calls a week, is for - ev - er and a

Invictus

WILLIAM ERNEST HENLEY

BRUNO HUHN

Out of the night that cov-ers me, Black as the pit from pole to pole, I

thank what-ev-er gods may be For my un-con-quer-a-ble soul.

a poco cresc.

yet the men-ace of the years,____

a poco cresc.

ff rit.

Finds, and shall find me un a - fraid.

Più mosso

sff *f col canto* *mf* *cresc.*

poco a poco rit.

ff

Con passione
mf

It

mf

Serenade

(Good-night! good-night, beloved!)

ETHELBERT. NEVIN

più rit.   *a tempo*

p

Thine eyes are___ stars of morn - ing,___ Thy

stacc. e sempre p

senza pedale

lips are___ crim - son flow - ers, Good-night! Good - night, be-

sempre p e stacc.

lov - ed, While___ I count the wear - y hours. Thine

eyes are stars of morn - ing, Thy lips are crim-son

flow - ers. Good-night! Good - night, be - lov - ed, While I

più rit.

count the wear - y hours.

Good- night.

Grow Old Along with Me

ROBERT BROWNING

MANA-ZUCCA, Op. 152

Grow old a-long with me The best is yet to be,

The last of life,— For which the first was made:— Our times are

in His hand Who saith, "A whole I

planned,

Youth shows but half;

Youth shows but half;

Trust God: see all, nor

be a - fraid!"

Marcheta

(A Love Song of Old Mexico)

Words and Music by
VICTOR L. SCHERTZINGER

Mar-che-ta, Mar-che-ta, I still hear you call-ing me
Mar-che-ta, Mar-che-ta, In dreams I can see you, your

back to your arms once a-gain,_____ I still feel the spell of your
sweet face with love all a-glow,_____ Your voice like soft mus-ic still

last kiss up-on me, Since then, life has all been in vain._____
ech-oes a-round me As in the old days long a-go._____

All has been sad-ness with-out you Mar - che - ta, Each day finds me
Come back, come back, dear, with you here Mar - che - ta, Then life once more

lone - ly and blue,_____ My poor heart is
joy - ful will be._____ The world's drear is and

brok-en, I want you, "Mar - che - ta", I need you "Mar -
lone - ly and sun - less, "Mar - che - ta", Your love was life's

che - ta" I do._____ Mar -
sun - shine to me._____

A Little Bit of Heaven

J. KEIRN BRENNAN

ERNEST R. BALL

Moderately, with expression

Have you ev - er heard the sto - ry of how Ire - land got its name?_ I'll
Tis' a dear old land of fair - ies and of won-drous wish-ing wells;_ And

tell you so you'll un - der-stand from whence old Ire - land came.__ No
no - where else on God's green earth have they such lakes and dells.__ No

won - der that we're proud of that dear land a - cross the sea,___ for
won - der that the An - gels loved its Sham-rock bor-dered shore,___ 'tis a

said, sup - pose we leave it, for it looks so peace - ful there! So they

sprink - led it with star dust just to make the sham - rock grow; __ 'Tis the

on - ly place you'll find them, no mat - ter where you go; __ Then they dot - ted it with sil - ver to

make its lakes so grand, and __ when they had it fin - ished shure they called it Ire - land.

After the Ball

CHAS. K. HARRIS

Have you no ba - bies, have you no home?_____
I wish some wa - ter; leave me a - lone!_____
I would not list - en, plead - ings were vain,_____

I had a sweet - heart, years, years a - go;_____
When I re - turned dear, there stood a man,_____
One day a let - ter came, from that man,_____

Where she is now pet, you will soon know._____
Kiss - ing my sweet - heart as lov - ers can._____
He was her broth - er the let - ter ran._____

List to the stor - y, I'll tell it all,_____
Down fell the glass, pet, brok - en, that's all,_____
That's why I'm lone - ly, no home at all,_____

I be - lieved her faith - less, af - ter the ball.
Just as my heart was, af - ter the ball.
I broke her heart pet, af - ter the ball.

Home on the Range

Cowboy Song

Whoopee Ti Yi Yo

Cowboy Song

Take Me Back to My
Boots and Saddle

WALTER G. SAMUELS
LEONARD WHITCUP
and TEDDY POWELL

Moderato

Take me back to my Boots and Sad-dle Ooh-ooh-ooh, Ooh-ooh-ooh, Ooh-ooh-ooh, Let me see that gen'ral store, Let me ride that range once more. Give me my Boots and Sad-dle, Let me ram-ble a-long the prair-ie, Ooh-ooh-ooh, Ooh-ooh-ooh, Ooh-ooh-ooh. Rop-in' steers on old "Bar X," With my bud-dies, Slim and Tex, Give me my Boots and

Deep in the Heart of Texas

JUNE HERSHEY

DON SWANDER

You Are My Sunshine

JIMMIE DAVIS and
CHARLES MITCHELL

Buffalo Gals

COOL WHITE

Allegro

1. As I was walk-ing down the street, Down the street, down the street, A
2. I stopped her and we had some talk, Had some talk, had some talk, But her
3. Her lips are like the oys-ter plant, Oys-ter plant, oys-ter plant, I
4. I asked this girl to be my wife, Be my wife, be my wife, Then

pret-ty gal I chanc'd to meet, O she was fair to view.
foot cov-er'd up the whole side walk And left no room for me.
try to kiss 'em but I can't They are so ver-y large.
I'd be hap-py all my life And skip to the love-ly moon.

CHORUS

Buf-fa-lo gals, Will you come out to-night, Will you come out to-night, Will you come out to-night?

Buf-fa-lo gals, Will you come out to-night, And dance by the light of the moon.

Carry Me Back to Old Virginny

JAMES A. BLAND

Waiting for the Robert E. Lee

L. WOLFE GILBERT

LEWIS F. MUIR

in'? Oh, what's that they're say - in'? The while they keep play - in', I'm
there? Say, were you a - roun'__ there, If you ev - er go __ there, You'll

hum-min' and sway - in'; It's the good ship Rob-ert E. Lee_
al - ways be found __ there; Why, "dog - gone", here comes my ba-

__That's come to car - ry the cot-ton a - way._____
by On the good old ship Rob-ert E. Lee._____

CHORUS

Watch them shuff - lin' a - long;_____

See them shuff - lin' a - long_____ Go take your

best gal, real pal, Go down to the lev - ee, I

said to the lev - ee! And then join that shuff - lin' throng;_____

_____ Hear that mu - sic and song;_____ It's sim-ply

great, mate, wait-in' on the lev - ee, Wait-in' for the

1.

Rob-ert E. Lee!__

2.

Lazybones

JOHNNY MERCER and
HOAGY CARMICHAEL

Slow Blues

Long as there is chick-en gra-vy on your rice, ev'ry-thing is nice.

Long as there's a wa-ter-mel-on on the vine, Ev'ry-thing is fine. You got no time to work, you got no time to play,

Bus-y do-in' noth-in' all the live-long day. You won't ev-er change no mat-ter what I say You're just made that way.

CHORUS

La - zy-bones, Sleep in' in the sun, How you 'spec' to get your day's work done? Nev-er get your day's work

done,   Sleep-in' in the noon-day sun.   La - zy-bones, sleep-in' in the shade,

How you 'spec' to get your corn meal made? Nev- er get your corn meal made.   Sleep-in' in the eve-nin'

shade.   When 'ta - ters   need spray-in',   I   bet you   keep pray-in'   the bugs fall off of the

vine _____ And when you go fish - in' I   bet you keep wish-in' The fish won't grab at your line.

La - zy-bones, loaf-in' thru the day,   How you 'spec' to make a dime that way? Nev- er make a dime that

(Spoken or sung)

way (well look-y here,)   He nev - er heared a word I   say!   say!

mf

rit

R.H.

Ped.   ✻

America the Beautiful

KATHERINE LEE BATES   SAMUEL A. WARD

The American Hymn
(Speed Our Republic)

MATTHIAS KELLER

The Caissons Go Rolling Along
(Artillery Song)

EDMUND L. GRUBER

O-ver hill, o-ver dale, We have hit the dust-y trail, And those
To the front, day and night, Where the dough-boys dig and fight And those

cais-sons go roll-ing a - long _____ "Coun-ter march! Right a - bout!" Hear those
cais-sons go roll-ing a - long _____ Our bar - rage will be there Fi - red

wa-gon sol-diers shout, While those cais-sons go roll-ing a - long: _____
on the rock-et's flare While those cais-sons go roll-ing a - long: _____

The Marine's Hymn

Arranged by Luis Guzmán
U. S. Marine Band

March tempo

1. From the Halls of Mon - te - zu - ma To the shores of Trip - o -
2. Our flag's un - furl'd to ev - 'ry breeze From dawn to set - ting
3. Here's health to you and to our Corps Which we are proud to

li; _____ We ___ fight our count-ry's bat - tles In the air, on land and
sun; _____ We have fought in ev - 'ry clime and place Where we could take a
serve; _____ In ___ many a strife we've fought for life And nev - er lost our

sea; First to fight for right and free - dom And to keep our hon-or clean;
gun; In the snow of far off North-ern lands And in sun - ny trop - ic scenes;
nerve; If the Ar - my and the Na - vy Ev - er look on Heav-en's scenes;

We are proud to claim the ti - tle Of U - nit - ed States Ma - rines. _____
You will find us al - ways on the job The U - nit - ed States Ma - rines. _____
They will find the streets are guard - ed By U - nit - ed States Ma - rines. _____

As published by "The Leatherneck"
with special Permission
of the
United States Marine Corps.

BRIEF BIOGRAPHICAL AND PRONOUNCING DICTIONARY OF COMPOSERS

Originally compiled by Albert E. Wier. Composers in Volume Nine added by John Tasker Howard

The following list contains the names of the principal composers, whose works are to be found in "The Scribner Music Library." Concise biographical information for ready reference has been given in most instances, also the pronunciation of foreign names on a simple phonetic system. Wherever possible, a systematic method of giving information has been adhered to, consisting of the surname, Christian name, pronunciation, nationality, field of effort, dates of birth and death (unless contemporaneous), and the name of best-known individual composition.

Abt, Franz (Ahbt). German song-writer, 1819–85. "When the Swallows Homeward Fly."

Adam, Adolph (Ah'dam). French comic-opera composer, 1803–56. "Si j'etais Roi."

Adams, Stephen. See Maybrick, M.

Albeniz, Isaac. (All-bay'niz). Spanish composer and pianist, 1860–1909. Many charming salon compositions.

Ambrose, R. S. American composer of sacred songs. "One Sweetly Solemn Thought."

Arditi, Luigi (Ahr-dee'tee). Italian composer and opera conductor, 1822–1903. "Il Bacio."

Ascher, Joseph. Dutch pianist-composer, 1829–69. "Alice Where Art Thou?"

Auber, Daniel (Oh'behr). French light-opera composer, 1782–1871. "Fra Diavolo."

Audran, Edward (Oh-drahn'). French light-opera composer, 1842–1901. "The Mascot" and "Olivette."

Bach, Johann Sebastian (Bahkh). German classical composer, 1685–1750. Church music, organ music, orchestral and chamber music, clavier pieces.

Bachmann, Georges (Bahkh'mann). French composer, 1848–94. "Les Sylphes."

Balfe, Michael. Irish operatic composer, 1808–70. "Bohemian Girl" and "Killarney."

Ball, Ernest R. American song-composer, 1878–1927. "A Little Bit of Heaven," "Mother Machree," etc.

Barnard, Mrs. Charles. See Claribel.

Barnby, Sir Joseph. English organist-composer, 1838–96. "Sweet and Low."

Beethoven, Ludwig van (Bay'toh-ven). One of the greatest German composers, 1770–1827. Symphonies, chamber music, and piano works.

Bellini, Vincenzo (Bell-een'ee). Italian operatic composer, 1801–35. "Norma," "La Sonnambula."

Bishop, Sir Henry. English composer, 1786–1855. "Home, Sweet Home."

Bizet, Georges (Bee'zay). French operatic composer, 1838–75. "Carmen."

Bland, James A. Negro composer and minstrel performer, 1845–1911. "Carry Me Back to Old Virginny," "Oh! dem Golden Slippers," etc.

Blon, Franz von. German bandmaster and composer of salon music, 1861– —. "Sizilietta."

Boccherini, Luigi (Boch-er-ee'nee). Italian cellist-composer, 1743–1805. "Minuet in A."

Bohm, Karl (Bowm). German pianist-composer, 1844–1920. "Still as the Night."

Boito, Arrigo (Bo'e-toh). Italian opera composer and librettist. 1842–1918.

Borodin, Alexander (Bor-oh-deen'). Russian composer, 1833–1887. Opera "Prince Igor," "Petite Suite" for piano.

Borowski, Felix. English-born American composer 1872–1956. "La Coquette," "Valsette."

Bosc, August (Bosk). French composer of light music. "Rose Mousse."

Bourgeois, Loys (Boor-zhwah'). 16th century French sacred-music composer, follower of Calvin. Writer of well-known hymn tunes.

Bradbury, W. B. American composer. 1816–68. "Sweet Hour of Prayer."

Braga, Gaetano (Brah'gah). Italian cellist-composer, 1829–1907. "Angel's Serenade."

Brahms, Johannes. One of the greatest German composers, 1833–97. Symphonies, chamber music, piano works, songs.

Bucalossi, Ernest (Boo-ka-loss'si). English dance-music composer. "La Gitana" Waltzes.

Cadman, Charles Wakefield. American composer, 1881–1946. Operas, orchestral music, piano pieces, songs.

Carey, Henry. English song-writer, 1685–1743. *Said* to have written "God Save the King," *known* to have written "Sally in Our Alley."

Carmichael, Hoagy. American composer of popular music, 1903– —. "Lazybones," "Star Dust," etc.

Chabrier, Emmanuel (Shah'br'ya'). French composer, 1841–94. "España," a Spanish rhapsody.

Chaminade, Cécile (Sha'mee-nahd). French composer and pianist, 1857–1944. Light piano pieces.

Chevalier, Auguste (She-val'ya). Brother of Albert Chevalier, the famous English coster singer, for whose songs (such as "My Old Dutch") he has composed the music under the name of "Charles Ingle."

Chopin, Frédéric. Polish composer, 1810–49. Romantic piano compositions.

Claribel (Mrs. Charles Barnard). English popular-song writer, 1830–69. "I Cannot Sing the Old Songs," "Come Back to Erin."

Clay, Frederic. English composer, born in Paris, 1838–89. Ballad operas and songs such as "I'll Sing Thee Songs of Araby."

Converse, Charles. American composer, 1832–1918. "What a Friend We Have in Jesus."

Cui, César. Russian composer, 1835–1918. Instrumental pieces: "Orientale," etc.

Czibulka, Alphonse (Tche-bool'ka). Hungarian bandmaster-composer, 1842–94. "Stephanie" Gavotte.

Debussy, Claude (Dŭ-bü'say). French impressionist composer, 1862–1918. Piano music, songs, orchestral works, opera "Pelleas et Melisande," ballet "Prelude to the Afternoon of a Faun."

Delibes, Clément (Deh-leeb'). French dramatic composer, 1836–91. "Sylvia" Ballet.

Denza, Luigi (Den'tsa). Italian song composer, 1846–1922. "Funiculi, Funicula."

Dittersdorf, Karl von. Austrian symphonic composer, 1739–99. "German Dance."

Donizetti, Gaetano (Don-i-tset-ti). Italian operatic composer, 1797–1848. "Lucia di Lammermoor."

Drdla, Franz (Derd'-la). Austrian composer and violinist, 1868–1944. His "Souvenir" and other salon pieces are very popular.

Drigo, Richard. Italian ballet director and composer, 1846–1930. "Les Millions d'Arlequin."

Duke, Vernon. Russian-born American composer of popular music, (real name Vladimir Dukelsky, under which he composes orchestral and concert music), 1903– —. "Brooklyn Barcarolle."

Durand, Auguste (Du'ron). French composer and music publisher for Massenet, Saint-Saëns, and many others, 1830–1909.

Dvořák, Antonin (Dvor'zhahk). Bohemian composer, 1841–1904. "New World Symphony" and a "Humoresque."

Dykes, Rev. J. B. English church-music composer, 1823–76. "Lead, Kindly Light," "Eternal Father, Strong to Save."

Eilenberg, Richard. Well-known German composer of dance music. "First Heart Throbs" Gavotte.

Elgar, Sir Edward. English composer, 1857–1934. "Pomp and Circumstance, "Salut 'Aamour," etc.

Falla, Manuel de (Fah'yah). Spanish composer, 1876–1946. Grand operas, "La Vida Breve."

Fauré, Gabriel (Foh-ray'). French composer, 1845–1924. "Romance Sans Paroles."

Faure, J. Baptiste (Fohr). French composer, 1830–1914. "Palm Branches."

Fibich, Zdenko. Bohemian composer, 1850–1900. "Poëme," popularized as a violin solo by Kubelik.

Field, John. Irish pianist-composer, 1782–1837. Nocturnes.

Flotow, Friedrich (Floh'toh). German operatic composer, 1812–83. "Martha."

Fontenailles, H. de (Fon-te-nah'yee). French composer of sentimental songs. "Obstination."

Foster, Stephen. American composer, 1826–64. Songs of the South such as "My Old Kentucky Home," "Old Folks at Home."

Franck, César (Frahnck). Belgian composer, 1822–1890. Church music, chamber music, "Symphony in D Minor," "Messe Solennelle."

Franke, Th. (Frank'eh). French composer of light pieces. "Intermezzo Russe."

Gabriel, Virginia. English song composer, 1825-77. "Only a Face at the Window."

Gade, Niels W. (Gah'de). Danish composer, 1817-90. Symphonies, Part Songs and Cantatas.

Ganne, Louis (Gahn). French composer, 1862-1923. Light opera and salon music such as "L'Extase."

Gaul, Alfred. English conductor-composer, 1837-1913. Cantata, "The Holy City."

Gautier, Louis (Goht'yea). French composer of light piano music. "Le Secret."

German, Edward. English composer, 1862-1936. Light operas and incidental music such as "Henry VIII" Dances.

Gillet, Ernest (Ghil'lay). French cellist-composer, 1856- —. "Loin du Bal."

Glazounov, Alexander (Glah-zoo-nohv'). Russian composer, 1865-1936. Symphonies and operatic compositions.

Glinka, Michail. Russian nationalist composer, 1804-1857. Operas, "A Life for the Czar," "Russlan and Ludmilla."

Gluck, C. W. von (Glook). German operatic composer, 1714-87. "Iphigénie en Aulide," "Orphée."

Godard, Benjamin (Goh-dahr). French composer, 1849-95. "Second Mazurka."

Goldmark, Karl. Hungarian operatic composer, 1830-1915. "Queen of Sheba."

Goodeve, Arthur. American composer of songs such as "Fiddle and I."

Gossec, Joseph. Dutch composer, 1734-1829. Operas and string quartets.

Gottschalk, Louis Moreau. American composer-pianist, 1829-1869. Piano pieces, "The Last Hope," "The Banjo," "Berceuse," etc.

Gounod, Charles (Goo'no). French operatic and sacred-music composer. 1818-93. "Faust" and "Ave Maria."

Granados, Enrique (Grah-nah'-dos). Spanish composer, 1867-1916, of piano music and operas. Drowned on the English steamship *Sussex*, which was torpedoed during World War I.

Gray, Hamilton. American composer of sacred songs such as "A Dream of Paradise."

Grieg, Edvard (Greeg). Norwegian pianist and composer, 1843-1907. Songs, pianoforte pieces, symphonies, etc.

Gung'l, Joseph (Goong'ul). Hungarian bandmaster-composer, 1810-89. "Oberlandler" Waltzes.

Hadley, Henry K. American composer, 1871-1937. Symphonies, operas, piano music, songs.

Handel, G. F. (Han'del). German operatic and oratorio composer, 1685-1759. "Largo."

Harris, Charles K. American composer of popular ballads, 1865-1930. "After the Ball."

Harrison, Annie Fortescue. English composer of semi-popular songs, 1849-1944. "In the Gloaming."

Hassler, Hans Leo. German organist and composer, 1564-1612. Church music. "O Sacred Head."

Hastings, Thomas. American composer and writer, 1784-1872. "Rock of Ages."

Hauser, Miska. Hungarian violinist-composer, 1822-87. "Cradle Song."

Haydn, Josef (Hide'n). German composer, 1732-1809. Oratorios, symphonies, and string quartets.

Heller, Stephen. Hungarian pianist-composer, 1813-88. "Tarantelle."

Herbert, Victor. Irish-born American composer, 1859-1924. Operettas, orchestral music, piano pieces.

Hérold, Louis (Ay-roh'd). French operatic composer, 1791-1833. "Zampa."

Hollaender, Victor. German comic-opera composer, 1866-1940. "Sumurun."

Hopkins, Edward John. English composer of Church music, 1818-1901. "Saviour Again to Thy Dear Name."

Howard, John Tasker. American composer and author, 1890- —. "Still Waters."

Huhn, Bruno. English-born American composer of songs, 1871-1950. "Invictus."

Humperdinck, Engelbert. German operatic composer, 1854-1921. "Hansel and Gretel."

Iljinsky, Alexander (Il-yin'sky). Russian composer, 1859-1919. "Cradle Song."

Ippolitov-Jwanov, Michael. Russian composer, 1859-1935. "Caucasian Sketches."

Ivanovici, J. (E-van-o-vee'kee). Roumanian bandmaster and composer of dance music, died 1902.

Jakobowski, Edward (Yak-o-boff-sky). Well-known comic-opera composer, 1858- —. "Erminie."

Jensen, Adolf (Yen'sen). German composer, 1837-79. "Murmuring Zephyrs."

Keller, Matthias. German-born American violinist and composer, 1813-1875. "The American Hymn."

Kerker, Gustav. German-born American composer of operettas, 1857-1923. "The Belle of New York."

Key, Francis Scott. Poet, 1780-1843. Author of "Star-Spangled Banner."

Kingsley, Charles. Noted English divine, novelist, and poet. Author of "Three Fishers."

Kistler, Cyrill. German opera composer, 1848-1907. "Kunihild."

Kittredge, Walter. American poet and composer. Born 1832. "Tenting To-night."

Kjerulf, Halfdan (Yha'rulf). Norwegian composer, 1815-68. "Last Night."

Knecht, J. H. (Nekt). German organist-composer, 1752-1817. "O Jesus Thou Art Standing."

Knight, J. P. English composer, 1812-87. "Rocked in the Cradle of the Deep."

Koschat, Thomas. German composer, 1845-1914. "Forsaken."

Lack, Théodore (Lahk). French composer, 1846-1921. Light piano pieces.

Lacome, Paul Jean Jacques. French light-opera composer, 1838-1920. Suite "La Feria."

Lassen, Eduard (Lah'sen). Danish composer, 1830-1904. "Thine Eyes So Blue and Tender."

Lasson, Per. Swedish composer of very popular piano pieces and songs.

Lavallée, Calixa (Lah-vahl-lay'). Canadian pianist-composer, 1842-91. "The Butterfly."

Lecocq, Charles (Lu-kohk). French light-opera composer, 1832-1918. "Giroflé-Giroflá."

Lehar, Franz. Viennese comic-opera composer, 1870-1948. "Merry Widow."

Lemare, Edwin H. English organist-composer, 1865-1934. "Andantino."

Leoncavallo, Ruggiero. Italian composer, 1858-1919. Operatic composer, "Pagliacci," "Zaza."

Levine, M. Russian composer of light piano music.

Liadov, Anatol (L'yah'-doff). Russian composer, 1855-1914. "A Musical Snuff-Box."

Liszt, Franz (List). Hungarian piano virtuoso and composer, 1811-86. "Hungarian Rhapsodies."

Lover, Samuel. Irish novelist, poet, and composer, 1797-1868. "Low-Backed Car."

Lowry, Robert. American hymn composer, 1826-1899. "Shall We Gather at the River?"

Luigini, Alexandre. French light-opera and ballet composer, 1850-1906. "Egyptian Ballet."

Macbeth, Allan. Scotch composer, 1856-1910. "Forget-Me-Not" Intermezzo.

MacDowell, Edward. American pianist-composer, 1861-1908. "Hexantanz," "Woodland Sketches," "Sea Pieces."

MacGimsey, Robert. American composer of Negro dialect songs, 1898- —. "Abraham."

Mana-Zucca. American composer, 1890- —. Piano pieces, songs. "Grow Old Along with Me."

Margis, A. French composer, 1874- —. "Valse Bleue."

Marie, Gabriel (Mar-ee'). French composer, 1852-1928. "La Cinquantaine."

Martini, Giambattista (Mahr-tee'-nee). Italian priest and composer, 1706-1784. "Gavotte."

Mascagni, Pietro (Mahs-kahn'yee). Italian opera composer, 1863-1945. "Cavalleria Rusticana."

Mason, Lowell. American hymn composer and music compiler, 1792-1872. "From Greenland's Icy Mountains."

Massenet, Jules (Mahss-nay'). French composer, 1842-1912. "Thais."

Mattei, Tito (Mat-tay'ee). Italian song composer, 1841-1914. "Non é Ver."

Maybrick, M. (Stephen Adams). English singer and popular-song composer. 1844-1913. "Mona."

Mendelssohn, Bartholdy, Felix (Men-del-soan-Bar-tole'dy). German composer, 1809-47. Symphonies, choral works, piano music, songs.

Messiter, Arthur Henry. English-born American organist and choirmaster, 1834-1916. "Rejoice Ye Pure in Heart."

Meyerbeer, Giacomo (My'er-baer). German operatic composer, 1791-1864. "Les Huguenots."

Meyer-Helmund, Erik. Russian composer, 1861-1932. Operas and piano music.

Millocker, Karl. Viennese light-opera composer, 1842-1899. "Beggar Student."

Molloy, J. L. Irish composer, 1837-1909. "Love's Old Sweet Song."

Monk, W. H. English organist-composer, 1823-89. "Abide with Me."

Moore, Thomas. Irish poet and composer, 1779-1852. "Believe Me If All Those Endearing Young Charms."

Moszkowski, Moritz (Mohsh-koff'sky). German (born Polish) pianist-composer, 1854-1925. "Serenata" and "Spanish Dances."

Moussorgsky, Modeste (Muhs-sorg'sky). Russian opera composer, 1839-1881. "Boris Godounov."

Mozart, W. A. (Mot'sart). One of the greatest German composers, 1756-91. Operas, symphonies, chamber music, piano works.

Nageli, H. G. Swiss music composer and publisher. Writer of well-known hymn tunes such as "Blest Be the Tie That Binds."

Nessler, Victor. German operatic composer, 1841-90. "Trumpeter of Sakkingen."

Nevin, Ethelbert. American composer of salon music, 1862-1901. Piano pieces, songs, "The Rosary," "Serenade," etc.

Nicolai, Otto. German opera composer and conductor, 1810-1849. "Merry Wives of Windsor."

Offenbach, Jacques (Of'fen-bahkh). French comic-opera composer, 1819-1880. "Tales of Hoffman."

Olsen, Ole. Norwegian composer, 1850-1927. "Serenade."

Paderewski, Ignace (Pahd-ref'ski). Polish pianist-composer, 1860–1941. "Minuet L'Antique."

Palmgren, Selim. Finnish composer and pianist, 1878–1951. Many popular piano works such as "May-night."

Parry, Joseph. Welsh opera composer, 1841–1903. "Blodwen."

Payne, John Howard. American dramatist, 1792–1852. "Home Sweet Home" (words).

Pierné, Gabriel (Pyair-nay'). French composer, 1863–1937. "Serenade."

Planquette, Robert (Plon-ket'). French comic-opera composer, 1848–1903 "Chimes of Normandy."

Pleyel, Ignaz (Play-el'). German conductor, piano manufacturer and composer, 1757–1831. "Pleyel's Hymn."

Poldini, Eduard (Poll-dee'nee). Hungarian composer of light piano music, 1869–1957. "Dancing Doll."

Ponchielli, Amilcare (Pon-ki-el'lee). Italian operatic composer. 1834–86. "La Gioconda."

Prokofieff, Serge (Proh-koff'ee-eff). Russian modernist composer, 1891–1953. Orchestral works, operas, piano music, "Peter and the Wolf."

Puccini, Giacomo (Poo-chee'nee). Italian opera composer, 1858–1924. "Le Villi," "La Boheme," "La Tosca," "Madame Butterfly," etc.

Rachmaninoff, Sergei (Rahk-mahn'ee-nof). Russian pianist-composer, 1873–1943. "Prelude in C Sharp Minor."

Raff, Joachim. German composer, 1822–82. Piano compositions.

Rameau, J. P. (Rah-mo'). French composer, 1683–1764. "Le Tambourin."

Ravel, Maurice (Rah-vehl'). French composer, 1875–1937. "Bolero," "Pavane," etc.

Reading, John. English organist-composer, born early part of seventeenth century, died in 1692. Supposed to have written "Adeste Fideles" (O Come, All Ye Faithful).

Rimsky-Korsakow, Nicholas. Russian composer, 1844–1908. "Sheherazade," "Le Coq d'Or."

Rodney, Paul. English composer of sacred songs such as "Cavalry."

Roeder, Martin (Ray'der). German composer, 1851–95. "Love's Dreamland" Waltzes.

Root, George F. American composer, 1820–95. "Battle Cry of Freedom," "Vacant Chair," etc.

Rossini, Gioacchino (Ros-see'nee). Italian operatic composer, 1792–1868. "William Tell" Overture.

Rubinstein, Anton (Roo'bin-stein). Russian pianist-composer, 1829–94. "Melody in F."

Saint-Saëns, Camille (San'sans). French composer, 1835–1922. Orchestral and piano compositions.

Sankey, Ira D. American evangelist and hymn composer, 1840–1908. "Ninety and Nine."

Scarlatti, Domenico (Skar-laht'ti). Italian harpsichord (antique style of piano) player and composer, 1685–1757. Various piano pieces and operas. .

Scharwenka, Philipp (Shar-ven'ka). German composer, 1847–1917. Piano pieces.

Scharwenka, Xaver (Shar-ven'ka). German composer, 1850–1924. Polish dances.

Schertzinger, Victor L. American composer of light music, 1890–1941. "Marcheta."

Schubert, Franz (Schoo'-behr). German composer, 1797–1828. "Ständchen" (Serenade), "Ave Maria," etc.

Schumann, Robert (Schoo'mann). German composer, 1810–56. "Träumerei," "Romance in F Sharp," etc.

Schütt, Edward (Shuett). Russian composer, 1856–1933. "A la Bien Aimée," "Romance." etc.

Schytte, Ludwig (Sheet-teh'). Danish composer, 1848–1909. Light piano pieces.

Scriabin, Alexander (Skreeah'bin). Russian composer, 1872–1915. Orchestral music, piano pieces.

Shostakovitch, Dmitri. (Shohs-ta-koh'vitch). Soviet-Russian composer, 1906– —. Symphonies, operas, piano pieces.

Sibelius, Jean. Finnish symphonic composer, 1865–1957. "Valse Triste" and "Finlandia."

Silcher, Friedrich (Zil'-yher). German song composer, 1789–1860. "The Loreley."

Sinding, Christian. Norwegian composer, 1856–1941. "Rustle of Spring."

Smetana, Bedrich. Bohemian operatic composer, 1824–84. "Bartered Bride."

Spendiarow, Alexander. Russian composer, 1871–1928. Piano music.

Stojowski, Sigismond. Polish pianist and composer, 1870–1946. Several piano compositions.

Straus, Oscar (Strous). Viennese light-opera composer, 1870–1954. "The Waltz Dream."

Strauss, Johann, Jr. (Strowss). Viennese composer, known as the "Waltz King," 1825–99. "Beautiful Blue Danube" Waltzes.

Strauss, Richard (Strowss). German composer, ultra-Wagnerian in form and harmony, 1864–1949. "Salome" and "Thus Spake Zarathustra," etc.

Stravinsky, Igor (Strah-vin'skee). Russian modernist composer, 1882– —. Orchestral works, ballets, "The Firebird," etc.

Sullivan, Sir Arthur. English composer of comic operas and sacred songs, 1842–1900. "Pinafore," "Mikado," "Lost Chord."

Suppé, Franz Von (Soop-peh'). German comic-opera composer, 1819–95. "Poet and Peasant" Overture.

Szalit, Paula. Scandinavian pianist, composer of many popular piano numbers.

Templeton, Alec. Blind English-born American pianist, composer, and parodist, 1910– —. "Mozart Matriculates," "A Lullaby," etc.

Thomas, Ambroise (Toe'ma). French operatic composer, 1811–96. "Mignon."

Thomé, Francis (Toe'may). French teacher, critic, and composer, 1850–1909. "Simple Aveu."

Tosti, Paolo. Italian singing-teacher and vocal composer, 1846–1916. "Goodbye," "Beauty's Eyes," etc.

Trotére, Henry (Tro-tare'). English song composer (Henry Trotter), 1855–1912. "In Old Madrid."

Tschaikowsky, Peter (Chi-koff'ski). Russian Composer, 1840–93. "Chant Sans Paroles," "Romeo & Juliet"; Piano Concertos; Symphonies.

Verdi, Giuseppe (Vair'de). Italian operatic composer, 1813–1901. "Rigoletto," "Il Trovatore," "Aïda," etc.

Wagner, Richard (Vahg'ner). The greatest opera (music drama) composer of all time, 1813–83. "Lohengrin," "Tannhäuser," "Tristan and Isolde," etc.

Waldteufel, Emil (Vahld-toi'fel). German composer of graceful dance music, 1837–1915. "Estudiantina," "Très Jolie" Waltzes, etc.

Wallace, William Vincent. Irish operatic composer, 1812–65. "Maritana."

Waller, Thomas (Fats). American Negro pianist and composer of popular music, 1904–1943. "A Handful of Keys."

Waring, Tom. American song-composer, 1902– —. "Ol' Darkie, Ol' Mule."

Webb, George James. English-born American composer of hymn-tunes, 1803–1887. "Stand Up for Jesus."

Webbe, Samuel. English church-music composer, 1740–1816. "Come Ye Disconsolate."

Weber, Carl Maria von (Vay'ber). German composer, founder of the romantic school of opera, 1786–1826. "Der Freischütz."

Wesley, Samuel. English organist and church-music composer, brother of Charles Wesley, 1766–1837. Composed several well-known hymn tunes.

Work, Henry C. American composer, entirely self-taught, 1832–84. "Marching Through Georgia."

Youferoff, Serge. Russian composer of piano music, 1864– —.

Yradier, Sebastian (Ee-rah-di-air'). Spanish composer, 1809–65. "La Paloma."

Ziehrer, Carl. German comic-opera and dance-music composer, 1843–1922. "Vienna Maidens" Waltzes.

A LIST OF IMPORTANT MUSICAL TERMS AND EXPRESSIONS

Compiled by Albert E. Wier

The following brief list of musical terms and expressions is designed to define concisely but plainly such musical terms, expressions, and abbreviations as are used in the music pages of "The Scribner Music Library." It is merely intended as a ready reference list in which the meaning of an unfamiliar term may be readily ascertained. The mark ' indicates the accented syllable of each word.

Aban'don. Without restraint.
A'bendlied. Evening song.
Accel. Abbreviation for "Acceleran'-do."
Acceleran'do. Increasing the speed.
Ac'cent. The emphasis of certain tones over others.
Acciden'tals. Occasional sharps, flats, or naturals placed before notes.
Accomp. Abbreviation for "Accompaniment."
Accom'paniment. The musical background to the principal part.
Acous'tics. The science of sound.
Ada'gio. Slow, faster than lar'go and slower than adan'te.
Ad Lib. Abbreviation for "Ad Lib'i-tum."
Ad Lib'itum. At will, play to suit your own idea of the time, or play or omit, according to your taste.
Agita'to. Agitated, hurried.
Air. A short melody, with or without words.
Al'bum Leaf. A short, simple piece.
Al Fine. To the end.
Allargan'do. Growing louder and slower.
Allegret'to. Cheerfully and quickly.
Alle'gro. Quickly, vivaciously.
Alle'gro Agita'to. Quickly and with agitation
Alle'gro Con Bri'o. Quickly with brilliancy.
Alle'gro Con Fuo'co. Quickly and full of fire.
Alle'gro Modera'to. Moderately quick.
Alle'gro non Trop'po. Not too quickly.
Alle'gro Viva'ce. Very rapidly.
Allelu'ia. "Praise the Lord."
Al Se'gno. "Go back to the sign," which means that the player must return to the sign *:S:* previously marked above some bar of the composition, and play from that measure to the word "Fine" or the mark ⌢.
Al'to. The female voice part next below the soprano.
Am'ateur. One who loves music and is proficient without practising it as a profession.
Amen'. "So be it." The usual ending of hymns, psalms, etc.
Amoro'so. Tenderly, affectionately.
Anal'ysis. The harmonic or structural dissection of a musical composition.
Andan'te. In a moderate tempo, with expression and grace.
Andan'te Canta'bile. Slowly and in a singing style.
Andan'te Con Mo'to. With an easy motion.
Andan'te ma non Trop'po. Not too slow.
Andan'te Quasi Allegret'to. Nearly as fast as "Allegretto."
Andanti'no. Less slow than "Andante."
Anfang. The beginning.
An'gelus. A bell rung in Catholic countries for prayers at morning, noon, and evening.
Anima'to. With life and spirit, animatedly.
An'them. A sacred vocal composition, words usually selected from the Bible.
A po'co. Gradually.
A po'co pi'u Len'to. A little slower.
A po'co pi'u Mos'so. A little quicker.
Appassiona'to. Passionately.
Appoggiatu'ra. A grace note or embellishment.
Arabesque'. A musical composition of ornamental character.

A'ria. A song or air, usually in an opera or oratorio.
Arpeg'gio. The notes of a chord played quickly one after the other.
Arrangement. The selection or adaptation of a composition from one form to another.
Articula'tion. Clarity of utterance in speaking or singing.
Artist. One who excels in musical performance.
Assa'i. Very, extremely.
A Tem'po. In time.
Attack. Method of beginning a musical phrase.
Aubade. Morning music.
Aus'drucksvoll. Expressively.

Ballad. A short, simple song.
Bal'let. A dancing pantomime, with musical accompaniment.
Band. A number of instrumental performers playing together.
Bar. The dividing line between two musical measures.
Bar'carolle. The song of Venetian boatmen.
Bar'itone. The male voice which is intermediate between tenor and bass.
Bass. The lowest male voice; the lowest part in a musical composition.
Bass Clef. The F clef, on the fourth line of the musical staff.
Bat'on. The stick used by the conductor of an orchestra or band.
Beglei'tung. An accompaniment.
Ben Marca'to. Well marked or accented.
Ben Tenu'to. Well sustained.
Ber'ceuse. A cradle-song.
Bluet'te. A short, brilliant piece.
Bole'ro. A lively Spanish dance.
Bourree'. An old French dance.
Brillan'te. Brilliantly.
Brindi'si. A drinking song.

Cabalet'ta. A simple melodic composition.
Cachu'cha. A popular Spanish dance.
Ca'dence. A close in melody or harmony, effecting a division into periods, or bringing it to a close.
Caden'za. A cadence or ornamental passage introduced near the end of a composition.
Cake-walk. A species of dance peculiar to the Southern negro.
Calan'do. Gradually diminishing in tone and growing slower in time.
Canta'bile. In a singing style.
Canta'ta. A secular or sacred poem set to music.
Cantile'na. A melody or air of a musical composition.
Canzonet'ta. A little song.
Capricciet'to. A short form of capriccio.
Capric'cio. A fanciful musical composition.
Caprice'. See "Capriccio."
Car'ol. A song of joy or devotion.
Cavati'na. A short simple song, or an instrumental composition of a song-like character.
Chaconne'. A series of variations in which the theme is merely a succession of chords which serves as a harmonic basis of each variation.

Chamber Music. Instrumental duets, trios, quartets, etc.
Chan'son. A simple vocal or instrumental composition.
Chant. A simple melody.
Chantant'. In a melodious or singing style.
Characteristic Piece. A musical composition with a distinct character.
Chorale'. A hymn-tune of the German Protestant Church.
Chord. The union of two or more tones played at one time.
Chor'ister. A singer in, or leader of, a choir.
Cho'rus. The refrain of a song. Also a company of singers.
Chromat'ic. Proceeding by semitones.
Chromat'ic Signs. Accidentals, such as sharps flats, or naturals.
Clas'sical Music. Music which has been accepted as standard.
Clav'ichord. See "Klavier."
Clavier. The French word for keyboard. See "Klavier."
Clef. A character used to determine the names and pitch of the notes on a musical staff.
Clef, Bass. The characters at the commencement of the staff, which indicate the names and pitch of the notes. The F clef.
Clef, Treble. The G clef, used in the upper staff of the piano score.
Co'da. The end of a piece, usually a few bars added in order to conclude a musical composition more effectually.
Colla Vo'ce. Follow the voice.
Commo'do. Easily, composedly.
Com'pass. The range of notes or sounds possessed by any musical instrument or the human voice.
Compo'ser. The writer of a musical composition.
Composi'tion. Any musical production.
Con Amo're. With tenderness.
Con An'ima. With animation.
Con Brav'ura. With brilliance.
Con Bri'o. With spirit.
Con Calo're. With warmth.
Concer'to. An elaborate instrumental solo piece with orchestral accompaniment, usually in three distinct or connected parts.
Con Dolo're. With pathos.
Conduc'tor. The leader of an orchestra or chorus.
Con Esp. Abbreviation for "Con Espressione."
Con Espressio'ne. With expression.
Conser'vatory. A school or academy of music, where every branch of the art is taught.
Consola'tion. A musical composition of soothing character.
Con'sonance. An accord of sounds agreeable to the ear.
Cresc. Abbreviation for "Crescendo."
Crescen'do. Increase in power of tone.
Crescen'do al diminuen'do. Increase and then diminish the tone.

D. C. Abbreviation for "Da Capo."
Da Ca'po. From the beginning.

Da Ca'po al Fi'ne. Return to the beginning and play as far as the word "Fine."

Da Ca'po Sin'al Se'gno. Return to the beginning, play as far as the sign, then play the "Coda."

D. S. Abbreviation for "Dal Segno."

Dal Se'gno. Repeat from the sign :S:

Dal Se'gno Alla Fine. Repeat from the sign :S: to the word "Fine."

Dead March. A funeral march.

Deci'so. In a decided manner.

Decresc. Abbreviation for "Decrescen'do."

Decrescen'do. Gradually diminish in power of tone.

Delibera'to. Deliberately.

Delica'to. Delicately.

Diato'nic. Proceeding in the order of the degrees of the natural scale.

Diato'nic Scale. The natural scale as represented by the white notes of the piano keyboard. There is, of course, a corresponding scale in every key.

Dim. Abbreviation for "Diminuen'do."

Diminuen'do. Decreasing gradually the power of the tone.

Dirge. A slow composition for use at a funeral or commemorative occasion.

Dis'sonance. A discord, opposite of "Consonance."

Divertimen'to. A short light composition.

Dol'ce. Sweetly and softly.

Dol'ce e Canta'bile. Sweetly in a singing style.

Dolen'te. Mournfully.

Dotted Double Bar. Dots *before* a double bar indicate that the preceding strain is to be repeated; *after* a double bar that the strain which follows is to be repeated. Dots on both sides indicate both styles of repetition.

Douce'ment. Sweetly and softly.

Doxol'ogy. A song of praise at the close of a religious service.

Elegan'te. Elegant.

El'egie. A funeral song or mournful poem.

Embel'lishments. Ornamental notes added to make a melody more effective.

Em'phasis. Particular accent on any one note, indicated by a sign.

Ener'gico. Vigorous, forcible.

Ensem'ble Music. Concerted music, played by a group of instrumentalists or vocalists.

Entr'ac'te. Music played between the acts of a drama or opera.

Espress. Abbreviation for "Espressivo."

Espressi'vo. Expressive.

E'tude. A study or exercise for the development of technique.

Execu'tion. Vocal or instrumental technical dexterity.

Ex'ercise. A composition aimed to develop technique.

Expression. Variations of tempo, phrasing, accent, volume of tone, etc., which render a performance of music expressive and meaningful.

F. Abbreviation for "Forte."

FF. Abbreviation for "Fortissimo."

FFF. Abbreviation for "Fortississimo."

Facilement'. With facility.

Fandan'go. A lively Spanish dance.

Fan'tasie. An imaginative musical composition.

F Clef. The bass clef.

Festi'vo. Merrily, gayly.

Fina'le. The last part of an opera or the last movement of a sonata or symphony.

Fingering. The method of applying the fingers to the keys, strings, or holes of different instruments.

Flat. A musical sign which, if placed in front of a note, lowers it a semitone in pitch.

Form. The architecture or structure of musical composition.

For'te. Loud.

Fortis'simo. Very loud.

Fortissis'simo. As loud as possible.

Forz. Abbreviation for "Forzando."

Forzan'do. Forcing, or forced.

Forza'to. See "Forzando."

Früh'lingslied. A spring song.

Fugue'. A classical form of musical composition.

Fune'bre. Funereal, mournful.

Funeral March. A march in slow tempo, for use at a funeral.

Fuo'co. Fire, passion.

Furio'so. Furious, mad.

Gai'ement. Gayly, merrily.

Gal'op. A quick dance.

Gavotte'. A stately and genial dance.

G Clef. The treble clef.

Genti'le. Elegant, graceful.

Gioco'so. Sportively.

Glissan'do. In a gliding manner, accomplished on the piano, by drawing the fingers rapidly over the keyboard.

Grace Note. An ornamental note or embellishment.

Grandio'so. Grand, noble.

Grave. A slow, solemn movement.

Gregorian Chant. The liturgical chant of the Roman Catholic Church.

Habane'ra. A slow Spanish dance.

Hallelu'jah. "Praise Ye the Lord."

Har'mony. The art of combining sounds into chords.

Hex'antanz. A fanciful composition depicting a witches' dance.

Hold. A sign ⌒ indicating that the period of sound or rest is to be prolonged.

Humoreske'. A playful musical composition.

Hymn. A religious song of praise.

I'dyl. A musical composition in pastoral style.

Impromp'tu. A fanciful composition.

Im'provise. To sing, play, or compose music at will.

In'terlude. The intermediate strain between the verses of a hymn or song.

Intermez'zo. A detached piece introduced between the acts of an opera. Also used as the title for any light, graceful composition.

In'terval. The difference in pitch between two musical tones.

Intro. Abbreviation for "Introduction."

Introduc'tion. The first measures in a musical composition which prepare one for the main part.

Jig. A light, brisk dance, popular in Ireland.

Klavi'er. The German word for pianoforte, but also applied to those keyboard instruments which were forerunners of the modern piano: clavichord, harpsichord, etc.

Lagrimo'so. Tearful.

Lamentan'do. Lamenting.

Land'ler. A country dance.

Lang'sam. Slowly.

Larghet'to. Not quite as slow as "Largo."

Lar'go. Solemn and slow.

Lar'go ma non Trop'po. Slow but not too much so.

Leg. Abbreviation for "Legato."

Lega'to. In a smooth manner, slurred.

Lega'to Touch. Sliding the fingers on and off the keys of the piano, holding down each note until the next is played.

Legere'ment. Lightly, nimbly.

Leggier'o. Light and swift.

Lent. Slow.

Lentemen'te. Slowly.

Len'to. Slow.

L. H. Abbreviation for "Left Hand."

Libret'to. The text of an opera, oratorio, etc.

Lie'beslied. A love-song.

Lied. A song or ballad.

Lied'er. Songs.

Lied'er Ohne Wor'te. Songs without words.

L'istes'so Tempo. The same tempo.

Loure. A slow, dignified dance.

Lul'laby. A cradle-song.

Mad'rigal. An elaborate vocal composition in three or more parts.

Maesto'so. Majestic, dignified.

Ma'jor. Greater, applied to intervals and scales.

Marc. Abbreviation for "Marcato."

Marca'to. Strongly accented.

March. A movement especially adapted for marching.

Marseillaise'. A French national air.

Mass. A sacred vocal composition.

Mas'tersingers. A class of poet-musicians in Germany.

Mazur'ka. A lively Polish dance.

Medita'tion. A religious composition usually instrumental.

Melodieux'. Melodiously.

Melody. A succession of tones forming a combination pleasing in sound and rhythm to the ear.

Me'no. Less.

Me'no Mosso. Slower.

Menu'et. See "Minuet."

Method. A system of instruction.

Met'ronome. An instrument for measuring the duration of notes.

M. M. Abbreviation for "Maelzel's Metronome."

Met'ronome Marks. Figures placed at the beginning of a piece of music, referring to the metronome.

M. F. Abbreviation for "Mezzo Forte."

Mezzo For'te. Moderately loud.

M. P. Abbreviation for "Mezzo Piano."

Mezzo Pia'no. Moderately soft.

Mig'non. Dainty, petite, charming.

Mi'nor. Smaller, applied to intervals and scales.

Minuet'. A slow, stately dance.

Misere're. "Have mercy," a prayer.

Misterio'so. Mysteriously.

Mit Bewe'gung. With movement.

Mo'bile. Movable, changeable.

Mod. Abbreviation for "Moderato."

Modera'to. Moderately.

Modula'tion. Transition from one musical key to another.

Morceau'. A choice musical composition.

Mor'dent. A musical embellishment.

Mos'so. Motion or movement.

Mo'tive. The theme of a musical composition.

Mo'to. Motion, movement.

Mo'to Perpet'uo. Perpetual motion.

National Music. The songs or dances characteristic of a nation.

No'bile. Noble, impressive.

Noc'turne. A dreamy, romantic composition.

Noël. A Christmas carol or hymn.

Non. "No."

Novellette'. An instrumental composition of romantic character.

Obbliga'to. A part added to a composition, in addition to the usual accompaniment.

Ode. An air or song.

Oh'ne. "Without."

Op'era. A drama or comedy set to music.

O'pus. The work of a composer indicated in the order of its inception or publication.

Or'chestra. A collection of string and wind instrument performers playing together.

Ornamen'tal Notes. Grace notes added to the regular notes of the measure.

O'verture. The preliminary instrumental portion of an opera. Sometimes a separate composition.

Pan'tomime. A wordless play with musical accompaniment.

Par'aphrase. A transcription or special arrangement of a musical composition.

Part. The music for each individual voice or instrument.

Part-Songs. Songs written in parts for different voices.

Pas'sage. Any phrase or short portion of a melody.

Pas'sion Music. Compositions of sacred character depicting the sufferings of Christ.

Pastorale'. A composition suggestive of country life.

Pathetique'. Pathetic.

Patrol'. A composition which imitates the approach and departure of a military body.

Pav'ane. A stately, slow dance.

Ped. Abbreviation for "Pedal."

Ped'als. The mechanism at the base of a piano which enables the performer to play with varying degrees of tone.

Perdendo'si. Gradually dying away.

Pe'riod. A complete musical sentence containing two or more phrases.

Phan'tasie. See "Fantasia."

Phrase. A short musical sentence.

Piace're (A). At pleasure.

P. Abbreviation for "Piano."

Piano. Soft.

Pp. Abbreviation for "Pianissimo."

Pianissimo. Very soft.

PPP. Abbreviation for "Pianississimo."

Pianississimo. As soft as possible.

Pitch. The location of a musical sound in the musical scale.

Pi'u. More.

Pi'u Alle'gro. More quickly.

Pi'u For'te. Louder.

Pi'u Len'to. More slowly.

Pi'u Mos'so. More quickly.

Pi'u Pia'no. More softly.

Pi'u Pres'to. More rapidly.

Pi'u Vi'vo. More lively.

Pizzica'to. In violin, or other bowed instrument, playing, plucked rather than bowed.

Placi'do. Calm, quiet.

Plus. More.

Plus Anime'. With more animation.

Plus Len'tement. More slowly.

Po'co. Little.

Po'co Ada gio. A little slower.

Po'co Alle'gro. A little faster.

Po'co Anima'to. A little more animated.

Po'co a po'co. By degrees.

Po'co a po'co Crescen'do. Gradually louder and louder.

Po'co a po'co Diminuen'do. Gradually softer and softer.

Po'co pi'u Mos'so. A little faster.

Pol'ka. A lively Bohemian dance.

Pol'ka Mazur'ka. A slow dance, in ¾ time, accented on the last or third beat.

Polonaise'. A Polish dance of stately character.

Pre'lude. A short composition of an introductory character.

Pres'to. Quickly, rapidly.

Pres'to Assai'. Very quick.

Pres'to ma non Trop'po. Not too quick.

Priere'. A prayer.

Pri'ma Don'na. Principal female singer in an opera.

Pri'mo. The word placed over the part for the upper player in piano-duet arrangements.

Pro'gram Mu'sic. Compositions which are inspired by, or suggestive of, scenes or stories which the music attempts to describe.

Pro'logue. The instrumental or vocal introduction to an opera.

Psalm. A sacred song or hymn.

Quadrille'. A French dance in five consecutive parts.

Qua'si. "Like."

Qua'si Allegret'to. Like an "Allegretto."

Qua'si Andan'te. "Like an "Adante."

Qua'si Pres'to. Like a "Presto."

Qua'si un Fanta'sia. Like a "Fantasy."

Rall. Abbreviation for "Rallentando."

Rallentan'do. Gradually slower.

Rapi'do. Rapid.

Rec'itative. Musical declamation.

Re'dowa. A Bohemian dance.

Reel. A lively Scotch dance.

Refrain'. The chorus of a song.

Religio'so. Religiously.

Repeat Marks. Marks indicating that a certain portion or portions of a piece are to be immediately played over again.

Re'pertoire. The operas well known by an opera company; the compositions well known by an artist or musical amateur.

Re'quiem. A musical service in honor of the dead.

R. H. Abbreviation for "Right Hand."

Rhap'sody. A fanciful musical composition.

Risolu'to. Resolutely, boldly.

Ritard. Abbreviation for "Ritardando."

Ritardan'do. Holding back the time.

Riten. or Rit. Abbreviation for "Ritenuto."

Ritenu'to. Held back.

Ro'mance. An imaginative vocal or instrumental composition.

Ron'do. A vocal or instrumental composition containing one constantly recurring theme.

Ruba'to. Taking part of the rightful time-duration of one note and giving it to another.

Salterel'la. An Italian dance in quick time.

Saraban'de. A slow, grave dance.

Scale. The succession of musical tones on which music is constructed.

Scherz. Abbreviation for "Scherzando."

Scherzan'do. In a playful manner.

Scher'zo. A playful composition.

Schnell. Quickly, rapidly.

Schot'tische. A pouplar modern dance.

Schlum'merlied. A slumber-song.

Score. The instrumental or vocal (or both) parts of a composition written on separate lines which are placed one under the other, so that the measures of every part may be read simultaneously by the conductor.

Score (Piano). A score in which the orchestral parts of an opera, etc., have been arranged so as to be played for piano solo.

Secon'do. The word placed over the part for the lower player in piano-duet arrangements.

Sec'ular Music. Ordinary music not sacred in character.

Se'gno. A sign :S: indicating a return to some previous part of the composition.

Semitone. The half of a whole tone, the smallest interval of the chromatic scale.

Semp. Abbreviation for "Sempre."

Sem'pre. Always, ever to a greater degree.

Sem'pre For'te. Ever loud.

Sem'pre Lega'to. Ever legato.

Sem'pre Pia'no. Ever piano.

Sem'pre Pi'u For'te. Ever louder.

Sem'pre Pi'u Pres'to. Ever faster.

Sem'pre Ritardan'do. Ever slower.

Sem'pre Stacca'to. Ever staccato.

Sentimen'to. With sentiment.

Sen'za Re'plica. Without repeat.

Serenata. A serenade.

Sextette'. A composition for six voices.

SFZ. Abbreviation for "Sforzando."

Sforzan'do, Sforza'to. With a sudden accent on a single note or chord.

Sharp. A musical sign, which if placed in front of a note, raises it a semitone.

Sig'nature. The name given the sharps or flats of any key.

Signs. Various symbols indicating certain details of musical performance.

So'loist. One who performs a vocal or instrumental composition alone or with instrumental accompaniment.

Sona'ta. An instrumental composition, usually containing three or four movements.

Sonati'na. A short, easy sonata.

Song. A vocal number.

Song without Words. Short, melodic instrumental composition.

Sono'rous. Rich in musical sound.

Sospiran'do. Sighing.

Sost. Abbreviation for "Sostenuto."

Sostenu'to. Sustained.

Spinet. An older form of the modern piano.

Stacc. Abbreviation for "Staccato."

Stacca'to. Detached playing of notes.

Staff. The five lines on which notes are written.

Ständ'chen. A serenade.

Stan'za. The separate verses of a song or hymn.

Step. A degree upon the musical staff.

String. Abbreviation for "Stringendo."

Stringen'do. Accelerating the time.

String Quartet. A combination of four stringed instruments such as violins, violas, cellos, etc. Also the name of a composition for same.

Style. The manner in which a composition is written.

Suite. A series of musical movements or pieces.

Sym'phony. An orchestra composition in several parts.

Tarantel'la. A swift Italian dance.

Tech'nique. The mechanical part of playing a musical instrument.

Tem'perament. The individual power of musical feeling in an artist or musical amateur.

Tem'po. Musical time.

Tem. 1°. Abbreviation for "Tempo Primo."

Tem'po Pri'mo. First or original time as marked on a piece.

Ten. Abbreviation for "Tenuto."

Ten'uto. Sustained, held.

Theme. The melody or tune of a piece.

Time. The measure of sounds in respect to their relative duration.

Time Sig'nature. The indication of the time (such as ¾) at the beginning of a piece.

Tone. A sound of definite pitch.

Touch. The method of striking the keys of a piano or organ.

Transcrip'tion. A special arrangement of a musical composition for some instrument for which it was not originally intended.

Transpose'. To remove from one musical key to another.

Träu'merei. A dreamy musical composition.

Trau'rig. Sadly.

Trem. Abbreviation for "Tremolo."

Tre'molo. Reiterating a note or chord combination with great rapidity.

Tres. Very.

Tres Anime'. Very lively.

Tres Fort. Very loud.

Tres Lente. Very slow.

Tres Pia'no. Very soft.

Tres Vi'te. Very quick.

Tri'ad. The common chord, consisting of a note with its third and fifth (for instance C–E–G).

Tr. Abbreviation for "Trill."

Trill. The rapid alternation of a note and the next note above, as long as the time of the first note endures.

Tri'o. A composition for three instruments; also the second part of a minuet, march, etc.

Turn. A musical embellishment, made up of the note above and the note below the principal note.

Two-Step. A popular American dance in ⁶⁄₈ time.

Tyrolienne'. A song or dance used in the Tyrol.

Valse. A waltz.

Var. Abbreviation for "Variation."

Varia'tion. The repetition of a theme in a new form while preserving the original melodic notes.

Varsovienne'. A dance in moderate ¾ time.

Velo'ce. Swiftly.

Vif. Lively, briskly.

Vigoro'so. Vigorously.

Viva'ce. Lively, vivaciously.

Vi'vo. Animated.

Volks-Lied. A national song.

Vor'spiel. Prelude, introduction.

Waltz. An animated dance in ¾ time, originating in Germany.

FOREWORD TO
THE COMPLETE INDEX

THE following complete index to "The Scribner Music Library" is primarily an alphabetical arrangement by titles of all the compositions, both instrumental and vocal, in the entire series of nine volumes. The titles of piano compositions are printed in Roman type and the titles of vocal numbers in italics. This arrangement will be found very convenient when you desire to ascertain whether a certain composition, either vocal or instrumental, is contained in the "Library." Instead of looking through the indexes of the different volumes, merely look it up in the complete index which will give you the volume and the page number if the composition is in the work.

For your convenience in ascertaining what compositions by some of the most noted composers, such as Bach, Beethoven, Grieg, etc., are contained in the "Library," most of these composers' names have been listed alphabetically, with such of their compositions as are in the volumes indexed under their names. This has not been done in the case of individual composers of lesser note, as the index would then become too cumbersome.

The titles of all operas from which selections or songs have been included in the "Library" are indexed alphabetically, and under each of these titles will be found the names of the individual numbers. For example, if one wishes the "Toreador Song" from the opera "Carmen," he will find it indexed under the title "Toreador Song," and also under the title of the opera.

A COMPLETE INDEX TO
THE SCRIBNER MUSIC LIBRARY